Trees
to Spot

Illustrated by Stephanie Fizer Coleman

Designed by Jenny Brown

Words by Sam Smith and Kirsteen Robson

Digital manipulation by Keith Furnival

You can use the stickers to fill in the chart
at the back of the book, so you can keep
track of the trees you have seen.

Many of the trees in this book shed their leaves in autumn and grow
new ones in spring. But some are evergreen, which means they lose
and grow leaves throughout the year, so they are never bare.

Towns and gardens

Leyland cypress
A dense, evergreen tree with sprays of scale-like leaves. Often planted as hedges.

Horse chestnut
Large leaves have a long stalk and 5-7 leaflets. Upright spikes of whit or pinkish flowers in May. Spiky cases with shiny brown, poisonous nuts called conkers from Septembe

London plane
Its shiny leaves turn golden brown in autumn. Clusters of hairy 'bobble fruits' hang on the tree through winter.

Norway maple
Elegant, green leaves turn gold before they fall. Fruits have leafy wings that catch the wind as they twirl down in October.

Common lime
Has jagged, heart-shaped leaves. Sweet-smelling, yellowish blossom in June-July. Hairy, green fruits with a wing-like leaf ripen in October.

Eucalyptus
Evergreen, silvery-blue leaves grow longer and greener with age. Small clusters of white flowers from June develop into woody cups full of ripe seeds.

3

Parks

Sycamore

Large, spreading tree with leather leaves. Its v-shaped fruits have papery wings to help them twirl and catch the wind as they fall.

Common walnut

Leaves of 7-9 small leaflets are bronze at first, then turn green. Smooth, green cases contain tasty walnuts in autumn.

Cedar of Lebanon

Look for round tufts of evergreen needles, and upright, barrel-shape cones in September. Branches spre out in flat, table-like layers.

Lawson cypress

Sprays of scaly, evergreen leaves smell like sour parsley. Look for pea-sized, brown cones in early autumn. Often planted as a hedge.

Whitebeam

Its large, toothed leaves are white and furry underneath. Look for clusters of creamy-white flowers in May, and red berries in September.

Monkey puzzle or Chile pine

Stiff, shiny leaves overlap all along its branches. Its bark is patterned with scars where leaves have fallen off.

Hedgerows

Common pear

Heart-shaped leaves have long stalks.
Has showy, white blossom in April.
Pears turn golden in September-
October, and are gritty to eat.

Crab apple

Rounded leaves have a
toothed edge. Has pinkish-
white flowers in May and
small, speckled apples in
September-October.

Hazel

Its floppy, hairy leaves
are almost round with a
pointed tip. Nuts ripen
in early autumn, if not
already eaten by squirrels.

Holly

Dark, evergreen leaves are glossy with thorny prickles. Look for small, white flowers in May and clusters of round, red berries in June.

Elder

Tiny, creamy-white flowers in June are heavily scented. Its small, purple-black berries in August-October are poisonous raw, but are cooked to make jam.

Common hawthorn

Shiny, dark green leaves with deep gaps grow on thorny twigs. Clusters of small, white flowers in May, and dark red berries from August.

7

Woodlands

Common beech

Oval, wavy leaves turn copper brown in autumn. Has small, green flowers in April-May. Ripe, triangular seeds drop from bristly cases in October.

Common ash

Each leaf is made of several small leaflets. Has purplish flowers in April and papery fruits called keys in October.

English oak

Curvy leaves have no stalks. Bark has knobbly ridges. Tall, rounded fruit called acorns ripen in October sitting in cups on long stalks.

Sweet chestnut

Look for spikes of yellow, mushroom-scented flowers in June-July, and prickly cases with glossy, brown chestnuts in October.

Wild service tree

Clusters of white blossom in May turn into oval, brown fruits called chequers in September. Green leaves turn rich red before falling.

Yew

Its flat, evergreen needles and black seeds are poisonous. Look for tiny green or larger pale yellow flowers in February-April, and red, berry-like cones in September.

9

Woodlands

Hornbeam

Its bark has upright, snake-like ridges. Clusters of green fruits wi leaf-like wings hold nuts that ripe in September, and spin as they fall A common street tree.

Larch

Tufts of soft needles turn gold before they fall. Pinkish, rose-like flowers grow in March, ripening into egg-shaped, brown cones.

Douglas fir

Soft needles that smell like grapefr grow around the twigs like bristle on a brush. Cones dangle down, wi three-pointed 'leaves' sticking out between their scales.

Silver birch

Its white, papery bark peels off in strips, and the branches droop. Look for long, 'lamb's tail' catkins in April-May.

Wild cherry

Reddish bark has slits across. Pointed leaves have jagged edges. Covered in white blossom in April. Birds eat its bitter cherries that ripen from red to black in July.

Small-leaved lime

Look for clusters of sweet-smelling, green-yellow flowers in June-July, followed by smooth, round fruits.

11

Near water

White poplar

Usually leans to one side. Leaves are furry and bright white underneath, and from far away the tree looks covered in snow.

Bird cherry

Dull green, oval leaves have finer 'teeth' than wild cherry. Drooping tails of small, white flowers in April. Birds eat the bitter, black cherries.

Weeping willow

Easily recognized by its thin, golden-yellow twigs that hang down to the ground. Long, narrow leaves have finely-toothed edges.

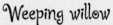

Crack willow
Slender, toothed leaves are shiny, dark green above, and blue-green underneath. Twigs break off easily and cleanly with a sharp 'crack'.

Aspen
Round leaves with wavy edges have long, flattened stalks. The leaves quiver in the slightest breeze, so you may hear them rustling even before you see the tree.

Common alder
Leathery, dark green leaves are rounded, and often dented at the end. Cone-like fruits drop seeds into rivers to help spread them.

13

Moorlands

Juniper

A small, bushy evergreen tree with sharp needles growing in threes around its twigs. Its bitter, blue-black 'berries' take up to three years to ripen.

Scots pine

Look for greyish-brown, flaky bark on the lower part of its tall, bare trunk. Bark is orangey higher up. Short, evergreen needles grow in pairs and its closed cones are pointed.

Field maple

Its small, slightly shiny leaves change to golden yellow in autumn. Fruits have papery 'wings'.

Purging buckthorn

This small, spiny tree has glossy, dark green leaves that curve inwards. Its small, purple-black berries shouldn't be eaten.

Blackthorn

Thorny branches are covered with a froth of white flowers in February. Its leaves appear in March. Blue berries called sloes ripen to black in September.

Spindle

Clusters of small, creamy flowers appear in May-June. It has bright pink, poisonous fruits in the autumn, when its shiny leaves also often turn deep orangey-red.

Swamps and wetlands

Swamp cypress

Feathery, light green needles
turn rusty orange before falling.
Round, purplish-brown cones in
October. In water, the roots have
woody growths, called 'knees',
that rise above the surface.

Downy birch

Similar to silver birch, but more
upright. The bark is pale browny-
white. Dull green, triangular leaves
have a round base and downy stalk.

Black poplar

Dark brown bark often looks
black, and is broken up by swollen
lumpy patches. Shiny, heart-shaped
leaves have a mild scent, unlike
white poplar.

...ay willow

...igs and leaves are very glossy.
...eenish catkins develop into
...uit capsules with tiny seeds
...tufts of white down which
...ch the wind.

Alder buckthorn

Branches and stems are smooth
and have no thorns. Berries
ripen from green to red, then
to dark purple or black.

...sier willow

...slender, glossy leaves have a
...zzy covering of silvery hairs
...derneath. Its smooth, yellow-
...een twigs are strong and
...xible, and used to
...ke baskets.

Uplands

Rowan

Often grows alone on mountainsides. Leaves are made up of 9-15 leaflets. Has clusters of creamy-white flowers in May, and shiny, red berries ripen in August.

Copper beech

Has red to deep purple, oval leaves. Woody fruits enclose one or two reddish-brown beech nuts.

Sessile oak

Unlike English oak, its curvy leaves have stalks. Its acorns, which ripen in October-November are egg-shaped, with very short stalks, or none at all.

Western hemlock

Flattened needles are green above and silver below. Small, brown cones are soft and droop from ends of shoots in October-November.

Wych elm

Very large, toothed leaves are almost stalkless, and have long points. Look for clusters of tiny, red flowers in February-March.

Sitka spruce

Its blue-green, flattened needles are very prickly. Its thin, creamy-brown cones have papery scales with crinkled edges.

Near the sea

Tamarisk

This untidy-looking tree has spikes of pale pink flowers in July-September. Tiny, grey-green scaly leaves make its twigs look feathery.

Holm oak

Dark, evergreen leaves are coated with pale hairs underneath. Young leaves are slightly spiny. Its small acorns turn red-brown when ripe.

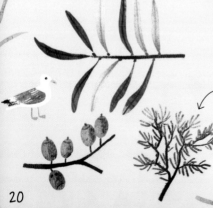

Sea buckthorn

This dense, thorny tree has narrow, silvery-green leaves. Female plants have juicy, orange berries known as seaberries.

Monterey pine

Slender, evergreen needles
grow in threes. Its fist-sized,
stubby cones are uneven
at the base and they only
open after forest fires.

Monterey cypress

Dense sprays of small, scale-
like leaves smell lemony when
crushed. Large, shiny brown
cones are roundish, with a
knob on each scale.

Austrian pine

Its long trunk often slants
slightly. Stiff needles grow in
pairs. Neat, narrow cones
open wide when ripe.

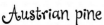

Spotting chart

Once you've spotted a tree from this book, find its sticker at the back, and stick it on this chart in the space below its name.

Alder buckthorn	Aspen	Austrian pine	Bay willow	Bird cherry
Black poplar	Blackthorn	Cedar of Lebanon	Common alder	Common ash
Common beech	Common hawthorn	Common lime	Common pear	Common walnut
Copper beech	Crab apple	Crack willow	Douglas fir	Downy birch
Elder	English oak	Eucalyptus	Field maple	Hazel

Holly	Holm oak	Hornbeam	Horse chestnut	Juniper
Larch	Lawson cypress	Leyland cypress	London plane	Monkey puzzle
Monterey cypress	Monterey pine	Norway maple	Osier willow	Purging buckthorn
Rowan	Scots pine	Sea buckthorn	Sessile oak	Silver birch
Sitka spruce	Small-leaved lime	Spindle	Swamp cypress	Sweet chestnut
Sycamore	Tamarisk	Weeping willow	Western hemlock	Whitebeam
White poplar	Wild cherry	Wild service tree	Wych elm	Yew

Index

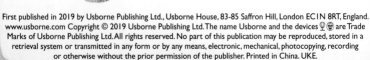